OUR
Valentine's Day
BOOK

by Jane Belk Moncure
illustrated by Mina McLean
and Carole Boerke

THE
CHILD'S
WORLD

ELGIN, ILLINOIS 60120

This book is about how we celebrated Valentine's Day in our class. You will have more ideas in your class.

Distributed by Childrens Press, 1224 West Van Buren Street, Chicago, Illinois 60607.

Library of Congress Cataloging in Publication Data

Moncure, Jane Belk.
  Our Valentine's Day book.

  (A Special-day book)
  Summary: A child describes the kindergarten's activities in preparing for St. Valentine's Day.
  1. Saint Valentine's Day—Juvenile literature.
2. Schools—Exercises and recreations—Juvenile literature. [1. Valentine's Day.   2. Handicraft]
I. McLean, Mina Gow, ill.   II. Boerke, Carole, ill.
III. Moncure, Jane Belk.   Our Valentine book.
IV. Title.   V. Series
GT4925.M64   1987   394.2'683   86-28387
ISBN 0-89565-343-5

1 2 3 4 5 6 7 8 9 10 11 12 R 96 95 94 93 92 91 90 89 88 87

OUR
Valentine's Day
BOOK

If I were a valentine,
Guess what I would do?
I would jump into a
  mailbox
And mail myself to you.
When I came to your house,
Guess what I would say?
"Will you be my valentine
  on Valentine's Day?"

Just before Valentine's Day, Andrea's dad brought us a big box. We used it to make a post office.

Miss Ballard cut the box and made a big window. Andrea painted the words, "Post Office," across the front.

Then we brought little boxes from home and made our own mailboxes. We decorated our boxes and put our names on them.

"I hope my box gets filled with valentines," said Andrea.

Next we made valentines. And we
made pretend stamps to paste on them.

Whenever the post office was open,
we could mail valentines. But no one
could open any until Valentine's Day.

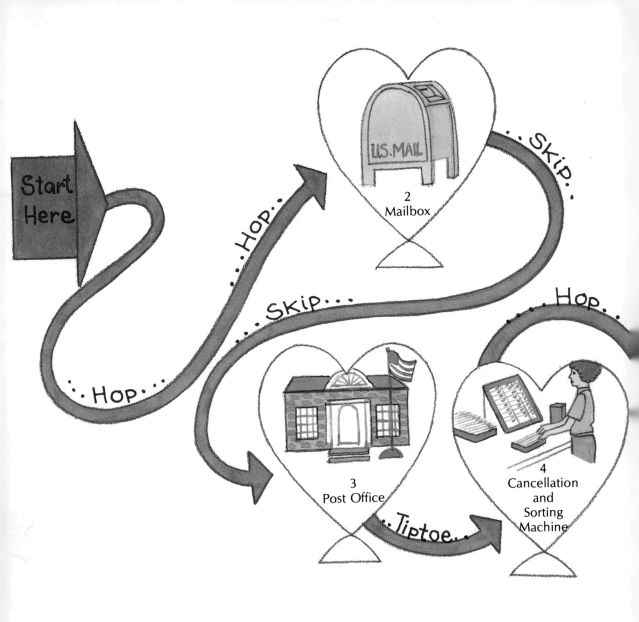

"We mail our valentines in our room," Miss Ballard said. "But most valentines take long trips when they are mailed. Today we will be valentines. Follow the signs around the room. Mail yourself as a valentine. See where you go."

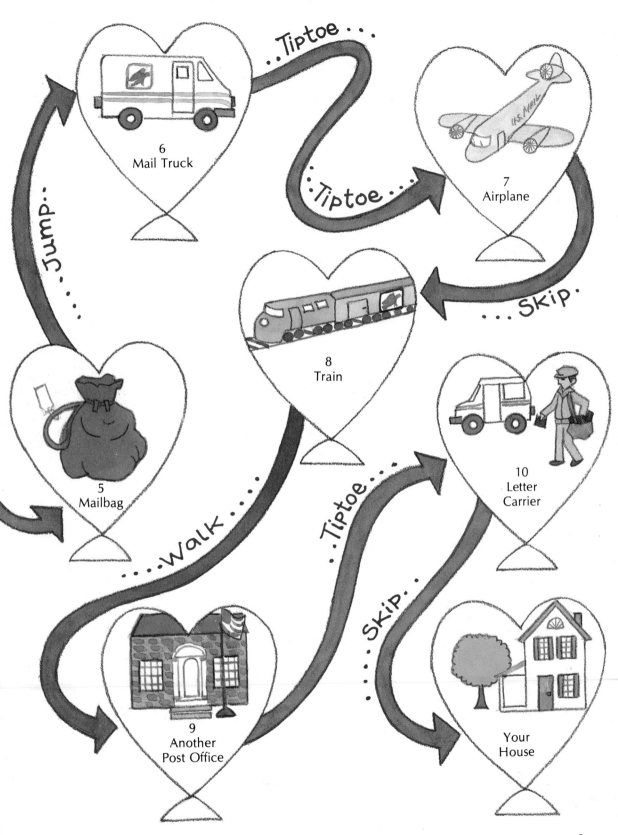

6 Mail Truck

...Tiptoe...

...Tiptoe...

7 Airplane

Jump...

Skip.

8 Train

5 Mailbag

10 Letter Carrier

Walk...

...Tiptoe...

Skip.

9 Another Post Office

Your House

9

At storytime, Miss Ballard showed us
her valentine mouse and his valentine
house. Then she put a ''guessing'' verse
on the wall.

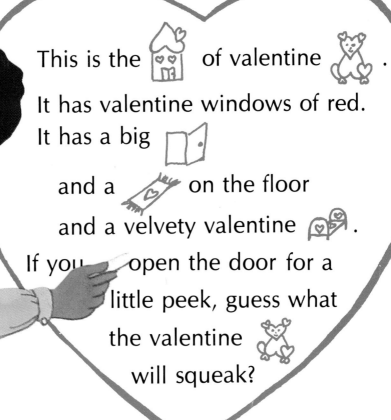

This is the 🏠 of valentine 🐭.
It has valentine windows of red.
It has a big 🚪
and a 🧧 on the floor
and a velvety valentine 🛏.
If you open the door for a
little peek, guess what
the valentine 🐭
will squeak?

We guessed lots of things. And we
made some mice too.

Our Valentine

Giraffetine

Whaletine

Dinosauratine

The next day, we made other valentine animals. We made up funny names for our animals. We filled the bulletin board with a Valentine Animal Park.

Animal Park ♥

Leopartine

Lionatine

Rabbitine

Peacockatine

An Elephantine

One day, Scott cut out a valentine puzzle. "I can make word puzzles," he said.

Others made word puzzles too.

Later, we put each other's puzzles together. And when we were done, we put each puzzle in a sandwich bag and kept it in our Valentine Word Box.

Little

Little

Little

Little

Miss Ballard showed us some valentine finger puppets, and we said this
valentine verse.

Little L was all alone, so

she went to play with Little O.

Then Little V came out to play

and so did Little e that day.

When all four letters stood in line,

they made a word for a valentine.

"I love puppets," said Amy. "I can make a valentine puppet out of a lunch bag."

When Miss Ballard put the scrapbox on the art table, Laura made a puppet too.

Later, Amy and Laura gave a puppet show for the class about a birthday party for the Queen of Hearts.

Andrea wanted to give her dad a picture for Valentine's Day. Miss Ballard showed her how to make a valentine mirror picture.

First Andrea drew her face on a round piece of paper.

Next, she cut out a paper mirror and pasted her face on it.

Then she turned the mirror over and wrote this on a heart for the back. . .

When I turn over my mirror,
I always see
someone who would like to be
    your valentine.

Andrea

When I turn over my mirror, I always see someone who would like to be your valentine.

21

The next day, Miss Ballard brought a little tree branch to school. "This is our valentine tree," she said. "Let's fill it with valentine leaves. Each leaf will be for someone or something we love. I will help you write the words."

Guess what? Everyone could read the leaves on our tree.

"Can we have a valentine party on Valentine's Day?" Amy asked.

"Yes," Miss Ballard said. "And we will invite guests."

So we made lots of things for our party. One group made placemats. Another decorated paper napkins. Others put hearts on paper cups and plates.

Then we each made a valentine crown for a king or queen of hearts.

Please come to our ♡ party on ♡ day at two o'clock.

Miss Ballard wrote the party invitation on the chalkboard. As we copied it, John said, "I will bring a special surprise to our valentine party."

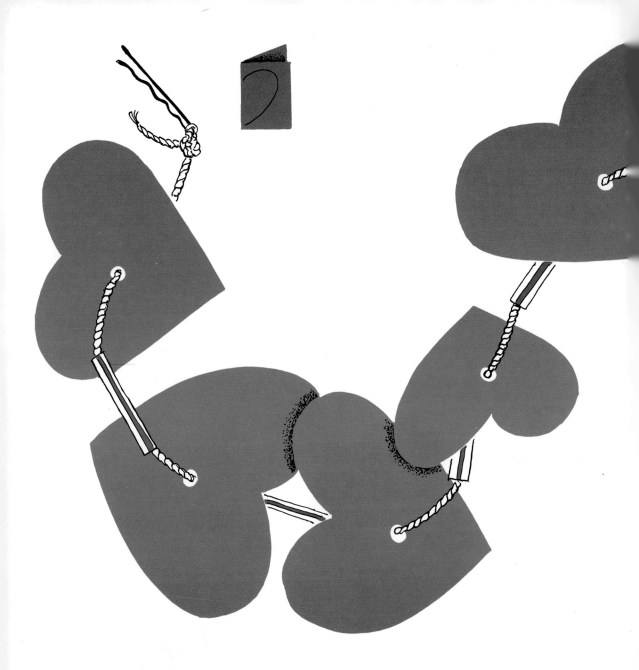

"In Hawaii, people give their guests necklaces of flowers," said Miss Ballard. "Let's give our guests necklaces of valentines."

Here's how we made them.

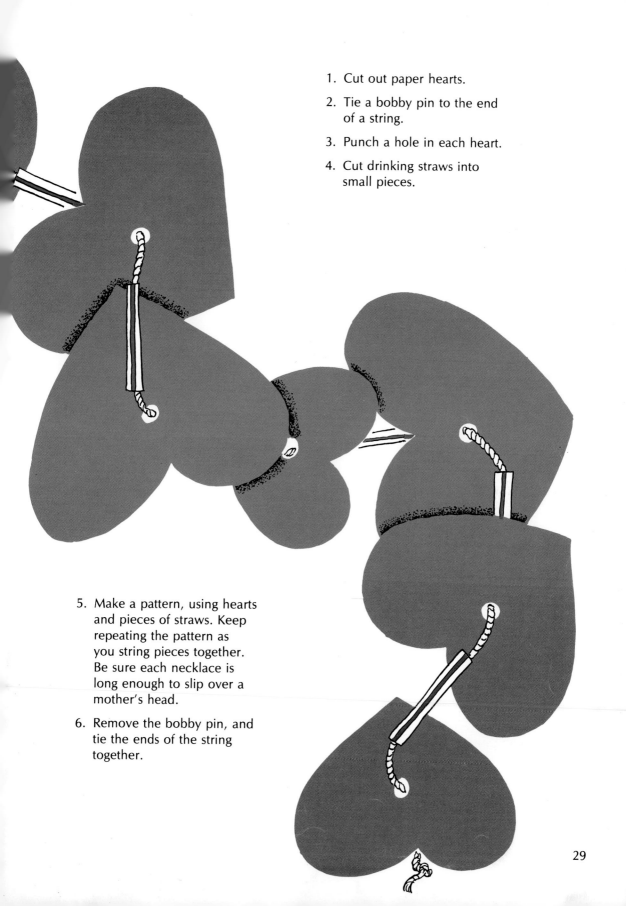

1. Cut out paper hearts.

2. Tie a bobby pin to the end of a string.

3. Punch a hole in each heart.

4. Cut drinking straws into small pieces.

5. Make a pattern, using hearts and pieces of straws. Keep repeating the pattern as you string pieces together. Be sure each necklace is long enough to slip over a mother's head.

6. Remove the bobby pin, and tie the ends of the string together.

At our valentine party, we served
cupcakes that we decorated ourselves.
We also served pink lemonade. Lots of
people came.

When it was time to open our valentines, Miss Ballard said, "Surprise. . . ."

In came John's mother. "I have some
mail for each of you," said Letter Carrier
Brown. "Happy Valentine's Day."